Published by Ravette Publishing 2003
Copyright © 2003 United Feature Syndicate, Inc.
All rights reserved.
Licensed by PSL
(www.snoopy.com)

PEANUTS is a registered trademark of
United Feature Syndicate, Inc.
Based on the PEANUTS® comic strip
by Charles M. Schulz.

Printed and bound in Great Britain
for Ravette Publishing Limited,
Unit 3, Tristar Centre,
Star Road, Partridge Green,
West Sussex RH13 8RA
by Cox & Wyman Ltd, Reading, Berkshire

ISBN: 1 84161 177 8

MY FIRST
2 in 1 COLLECTION
CONTAINS:

THE FLYING ACE
THE LITERARY ACE

SNOOPY

(features as)

The Flying Ace

Charles M. Schulz

HERE'S THE "LONE BEAGLE" BACK HOME AFTER HIS HISTORIC FLIGHT FROM NEW YORK TO PARIS...

RIDING THROUGH THE CITY, HE IS GREETED BY CHEERING THRONGS IN A HUGE TICKER TAPE PARADE...

10-25

A ONE TICKER TAPE PARADE..

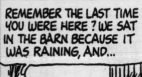

© 1980 United Feature Syndicate, Inc. 8-12

STAY RIGHT WHERE YOU ARE, OR I'LL POUND YOU!

THIS IS GOING TO BE HARD TO DO...

3-17

© 1984 United Feature Syndicate, Inc.

SNOOPY

(features as)

The Literary Ace

Charles M. Schulz

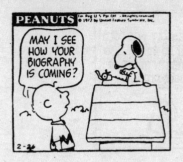

PEANUTS

Things I've Learned
After It Was Too Late

6-28

Never argue with the cat
next door. He's always right

PEANUTS

Though her husband often went on business trips, she hated to be left alone.

"I've solved our problem," he said. "I've bought you a St. Bernard. It's name is Great Reluctance."

"Now, when I go away, you shall know that I am leaving you with Great Reluctance!"

She hit him with a waffle iron.

PEANUTS

His wife had always hated his work.

9-18

"You'll never make any money growing toadstools," she complained.

"On the contrary," he declared. "My toadstool business is mushrooming!"

She creamed him with the electric toaster.

and I am including postage for the return of my story if you don't buy it.

Then again, why should I send postage for its' return when I am sure you are going to buy it?

On the other hand, maybe I'd better send it, but then again, why should I? On the other hand, maybe I should, but then again

FORGET IT!

PEANUTS

Dutch Waltz, the famous skater, was worried.

His skating partner, Chil Blain, was in love.

While playing a show in Denver, she had become involved with a cowboy named Martin Gale.

THE STORY ISN'T MUCH, BUT THE NAMES ARE GREAT!

4-2

SCHULZ

PEANUTS

Immediately after he won the golf tournament, he was interviewed on TV.

"This is the most exciting moment of my life!" he said.

"I saw you on TV," said his wife. "I thought the day we got married was the most exciting moment of your life."

In his next tournament, he failed to make the cut.

4-4

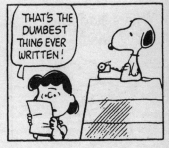

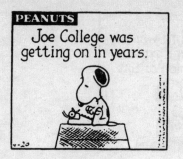

PEANUTS

Joe College was getting on in years.

Where had the time gone?

It was hard to believe that he had a son old enough to graduate from High School.

Joe Junior College.

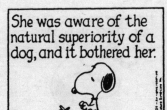

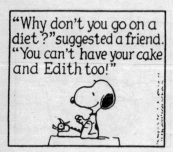

PEANUTS

The curtain of night enveloped the fleeing lovers.

Though fiery trials had threatened, oceans of longing had kept them together.

Now, a new icicle of terror stabbed at the embroidery of their existence.

JOE METAPHOR!

Joe Swimming ran a pool service.

When he and his wife had their first daughter, they couldn't decide on a name.

"How about Chlorine?" suggested Joe.

His wife hit him with a pool sweep.

Gentlemen,
    Regarding the recent rejection slip you sent me.

I think there might have been a misunderstanding.

What I really wanted was for you to publish my story, and send me fifty thousand dollars.

Didn't you realize that?

Dear Son,

Thank you for considering us with your letter.

We regret, however, that it does not suit our present needs. Sincerely, Mother

EVEN MY LETTERS HOME GET REJECTED!

3-13

They could never agree on anything.

4-6

"Why don't we truck on down to the bike shop?" she asked.

"No," he said. "Let's bike on down to the truck shop."

© 1982 United Feature Syndicate, Inc.

Their marriage counselor was not at all encouraging.

SCHULZ

Spring.

3-27

We know that Spring is near when it begins to get

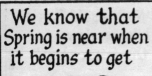

windy.

Beauty Tips

5-4

How to look
younger...

© 1982 United Feature Syndicate, Inc.

Don't be born
so soon.

SCHULZ

Beauty Tips

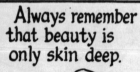

Always remember that beauty is only skin deep.

© 1982 United Feature Syndicate, Inc.

5-10

fur deep.

Beauty Tips

Always remember that beauty is only fur deep.

5-11

© 1982 United Feature Syndicate, Inc.

feather deep.

Travel Tips

How to avoid
carsickness, seasickness
and airsickness...

Be careful what
you eat.

And stay home.

Travel Tips...
"Arriving Home"

When putting away your luggage after arriving home, always close the zippers so bugs can't crawl in.

THAT'S THE DUMBEST TRAVEL TIP I'VE EVER READ!

IT'S NOT SO BAD WHEN YOU CONSIDER I'VE NEVER BEEN ANYWHERE...

9-20

He was a huge man
with a fierce and wild
expression, and eyes

like

a teeny tiny
little yellow bird.

© 1984 United Feature Syndicate, Inc.   11-30